The VERY MERRY CHRISTMAS ACTIVITY Book

ARCTURUS

ARCTURUS

This edition published in 2018 by Arcturus Publishing Limited
26/27 Bickels Yard, 151–153 Bermondsey Street,
London SE1 3HA

ISBN: 978-1-78828-275-8
CH006026NT
Supplier 29, Date 0718, Print run 7425

Illustrations: Shutterstock
Author: JMS Books llp
Designer: Chris Bell, cbdesign

Printed in China

Season's Greetings!

We hope you enjoy **The Very Merry Christmas Activity Book.**
It's packed with drawing activities, fun puzzles, and games to keep you busy
all season long. So grab your pens and pencils and begin right away!
If you get stuck on any puzzles, the answers are on pages 86-96.

Why don't you start by decorating this pretty Christmas tree?

NUTTY NUTCRACKERS

Can you work out which of these nutcracker
soldiers is different from the rest?

Stained glass angel

Shade in this stained glass angel
using the numbers as a guide.

merry maze

Can you help Santa reach his sack of presents?

Fir tree forest

Which of these Christmas trees does not have a matching pair?

7

A bird in the hand...

Can you work out which is the correct shadow for this festive bluebird?

TOY-DOKU

Draw in the toys to complete the sudoku.
Each row, column, and mini-grid should
contain one of each item.

Quick on the draw!

Learn how to draw a Christmas tree in four easy steps.

1 First, draw three overlapping triangles, each one a little bigger than the last.

2 Erase the overlapping lines and add a long shape for the trunk.

3 Add a star at the top and some circles for the pretty baubles.

4 Finish off the tree with your brightest crayons or pencils.

You can learn to draw me on page 30!

10

COOKIE TIME!

Santa wants to get to his cookies and milk.
Can you help him find them?
Follow the strings carefully!

a b c

FESTIVE FROLICS

Which festive item appears only once?

SNOW JOKE

Use your brightest pencils to complete this picture of a snowman having fun.

SNOWMAN GRID

Here's an easy way to draw a snowman.
Just copy the picture on the right into
the grid below, square by square.

LET IT SNOW!

SLEIGH RIDE

There are six differences between these two pictures of Santa and his sleigh. Can you find them all?

Dotty dilemma

Join the dots to see who has come
to visit her woodland pals.

10
12　　13　　14
11　　　　　　　　15　　16

9

8　　　　　　　　　　　17

　　　　　　　　　　18

7　　　　　　　　　19

6　5
33　　　　　　　　1　20
　　4　3　2

32　　　　　　　　　　　21
31　　　　　　　　22
　27　26　　23
30　　　　　　23
29　28　25　24

Trim the tree...

Make this Christmas tree really festive by adding baubles, lights, ornaments, candy canes, and, of course, a star on the top!

Muffin mayhem

a tealcocho

b barpyrers

c lebbyreru

d livanal

e rwasytrerb

f naabna

Twinkle has baked some muffins for her elf pals, but the labels have got muddled. Can you help her unscramble the letters to reveal the ingredients?

The real Rudolph

Some rascally reindeer have put on false red noses to try to trick Santa. Can you help him work out which is the real Rudolph?

1. Rudolph does not have black antlers.
2. Rudolph has a bell.
3. Rudolph has brown hooves.
4. Rudolph does not have a blue collar.

STUFFED STOCKINGS

Look carefully at the order of the three Christmas stockings on the right. How many times can you find them in exactly the same order in the box? Search from left to right, and from top to bottom.

Jingle Bells

start →

25	10	21	45	16
33	26	60	43	50
11	35	40	20	38
8	5	47	14	44
19	28	30	55	→ finish

Can you find a path through the bells using only numbers from the five times table? Remember, they are all multiples of five. Move up, down, sideways, and diagonally.

Birds of a feather

Finish this picture of birds in the snow.

SNOW TIME!

Each of these snowmen is different from the others.
Can you spot why?

Secret Silhouette

Shade in all the fragments containing a red dot to reveal the picture.

Boot-iful boots

Santa is tired of his old black boots and wants to buy a cool new pair.

The top box shows all the styles he can choose from. He has picked one style, but left all the rest jumbled up in the bottom box. Can you work out which one he has bought?

MAZE DAZE

Can you help the king reach the manger?

IT'S A GIFT...

a. NARIT

b. DYEDT

c. LALB

d. LODYL

e. SKIBRC

f. YOT RCA

Roger the elf has muddled up the labels on these presents. Can you help him work out which of the toys below is in each box?

SOCK IT TO ME!

These clever robins have noticed that something is missing from the bottom washing line. Can you spot which sock does not have a matching pair?

PENGUINS ON PARADE

Learn how to draw a penguin in four easy steps!

 **1** First, draw two overlapping circles, one for his head and a slightly smaller one for his body.

 **2** Give him a black head with a point in the middle and make his chest and face white.

 **3** Add his little black wings and tiny orange feet.

 **4** He needs a cute face and beak. Give him a smart bow tie to finish.

Add a snazzy scarf...

...or a pretty pink bow.

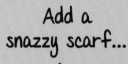

Woodland wonder

There are six differences between these two pictures of woodland creatures. Can you find them all?

Sleigh bells in the snow

Can you find the correct shadow for Santa's sleigh ride?

Candy quest

How many candy canes can you spot?

Christmas fairies

Which of these pretty fairies is going to take pride of place at the top of the tree? Read the clues carefully before making your choice.

1. She is holding a wand.
2. She is not wearing a crown.
3. She has a cute bow in her hair.
4. Her shoes match her dress.

Festive folk

Draw a circle around the odd one out in each row.

ALL WRAPPED UP

Look carefully at the three parcels on the right.
Can you find them in exactly the same order six times
in the box below? Search from left to right, right to left,
top to bottom, and from the bottom up!

IT'S A CINCH!

This penguin is easy to draw. Simply copy the picture on the right into the grid below, one square at a time.

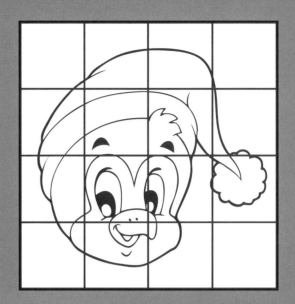

Shad-oku time!

Draw in the shapes to complete the sudoku.
Each row, column, and mini-grid should
contain one of each item.

Cool shades

1 2 3 4 5 6

Paint this cheerful snowman
using the numbers as a guide.

Knotty problem

This cheeky monkey has got in a real tangle wrapping his present! Can you help him find the end of the ribbon so that he can finish the bow?

Poles apart!

These polar bears may look identical at first glance, but each one differs in one small way from his pals. Can you spot the differences?

SWEET TOOTH

Rudolph loves candy far too much!
The elves have mixed up the labels to
stop him munching too fast. Can you
help him unscramble the letters?

a genroa

b olac

c nitm

d lump

e imel

f omeln

Gorgeous garland

Make this yuletide wreath look really pretty with baubles, bows, and flowers.

Counting stars

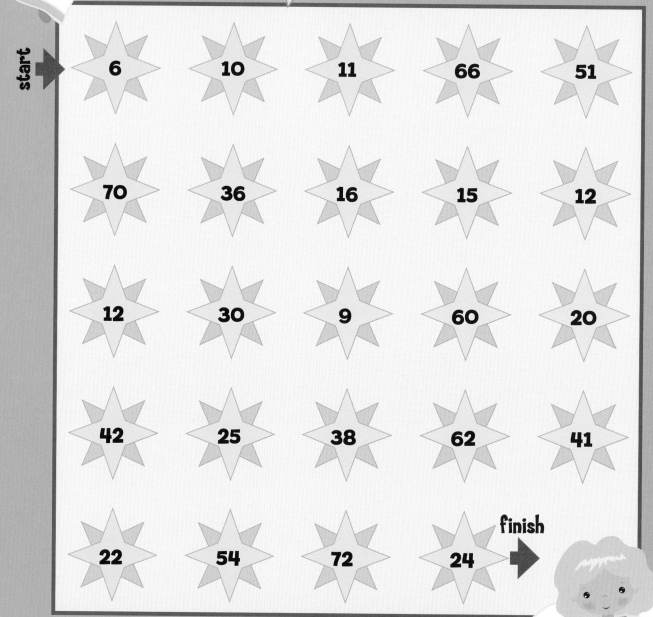

start →

6	10	11	66	51
70	36	16	15	12
12	30	9	60	20
42	25	38	62	41
22	54	72	24	

finish →

Using only multiples of six, find a path through the bells.
Remember, all of the numbers are in the six times table.

SHADOW PUPPETS

Can you work out which is the correct shadow for this playful puppet?

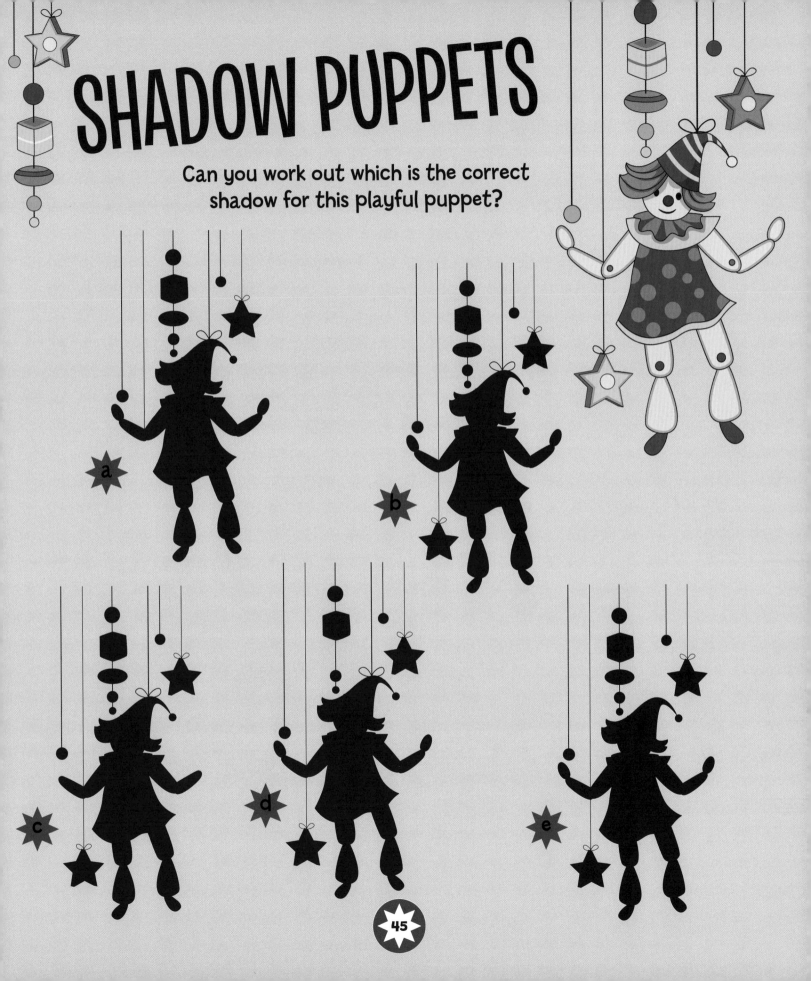

TOY STORY

Draw a circle around the odd one out in each row.

We Three Kings...

The Wise Men have journeyed far, but six of these kings are imposters! Can you work out which are the real Wise Men and what is wrong with the others?

Cookies galore!

Which four tasty cookies appear more than twice in the box below?

QUICK ON THE DRAW

Here's an easy way to draw Rudolph. Just copy the picture in the grid square by square into the box below.

RING-A-DING

Complete this picture of the bells decorating a Christmas tree.

Snow globe poser

Look carefully at the snow
globe, then try answering
the questions on
the next page.

SNOW GLOBE POSER QUESTIONS

1. How many windows does the house have?

2. How many "buttons" are on the snowman's chest?

3. What can be seen in the window, top left?

4. What is hanging on the front door?

5. What is the snowman holding?

Don't be tempted to turn the page for a quick peek!

Look through the window

Paint this stained glass window
using the numbers as a guide.

A-MAZE-ING !

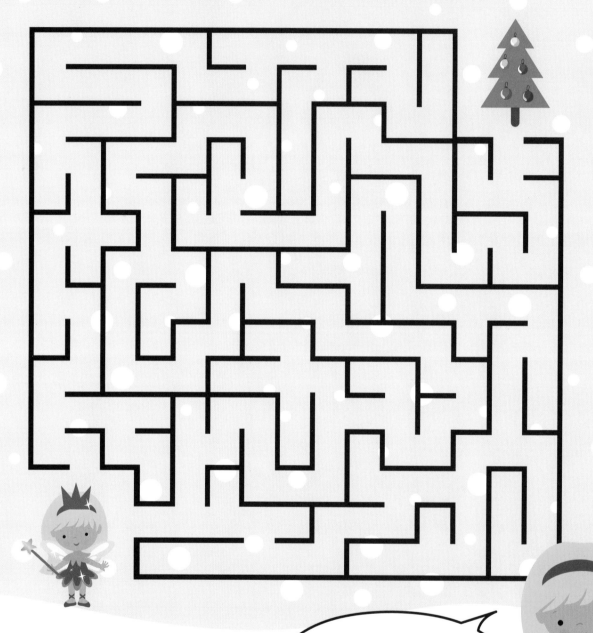

Can you help the fairy find her way back to the Christmas tree?

54

Nutcracker army

Which of the nutcracker soldiers in the panel below appears more than once?

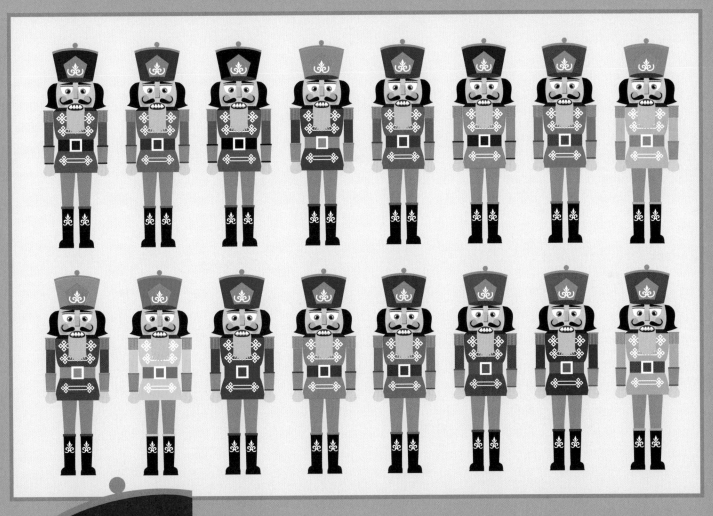

All present and correct?

Yes, sir!

MONKEY PUZZLE

Can you work out which of these playful monkeys is different from the rest?

Beautiful baubles

Design your own Christmas decorations. Try spots, stripes, stars, or wavy lines. Or draw a picture on them if you prefer!

Candy-doku

Draw in the correct candy to complete the sudoku. Each row, column, and mini-grid should contain one of each item.

WHILE SHEPHERDS WATCHED...

These shepherds having been watching their flocks all night, but one sheep has gone missing. Can you find the sheep that does not have a matching pair?

59

Missing piece...

a

b

c

d

Can you work out which of the segments is the missing piece?
When you have found it, draw it in.

WINTER WONDERLAND

There are six differences between these two snowy village scenes. Can you find them all?

Get your skates on!

The snowmen are having great fun on the ice.
Can you spot the two that are identical?
(Clue: they may not be looking in the same direction.)

NUMBER FUN

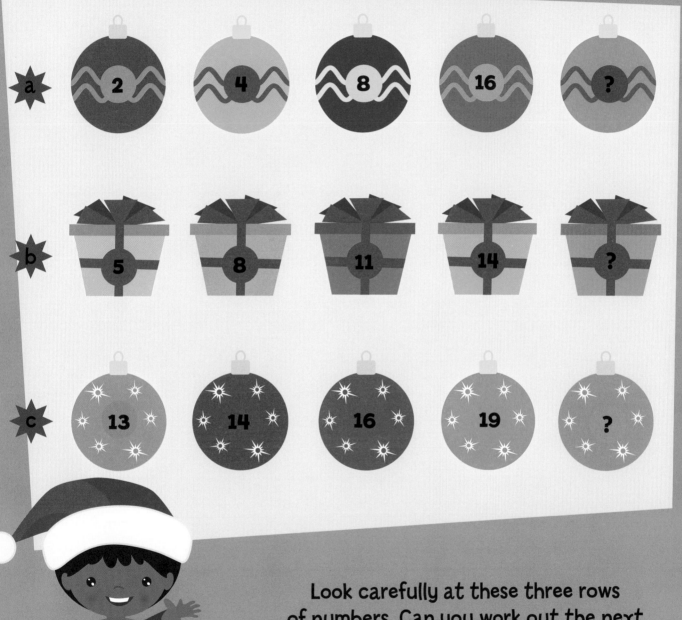

a 2 4 8 16 ?

b 5 8 11 14 ?

c 13 14 16 19 ?

Look carefully at these three rows
of numbers. Can you work out the next
in the sequence in each row?

Ring the changes

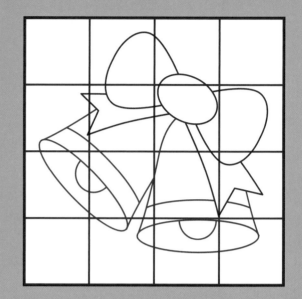

You can learn to draw these Christmas bells super speedily! Just copy the picture into the grid below square by square.

MAKING TRACKS

Good King Wenceslas has been out walking in the snow and has found some animal tracks. Can you draw lines to match each animal with its footprint?

Puppet on a string

Robin the elf has really tangled up the strings of this puppet. Can you help him find the correct string?

Toys galore!

Finish this picture of a toy box and then decide which toy you would play with.

SWEET TREATS

Look carefully at the order of the three tasty Christmas treats below.
Can you find them in exactly the same order in the box? Search from
left to right and top to bottom, and you will find them only once!

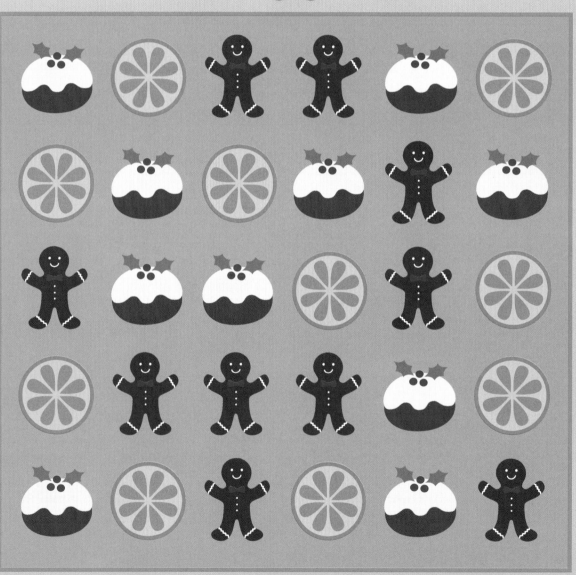

Feathered friend

Learn how to draw a wise owl in four easy steps.

1

First, draw two overlapping oval shapes, a big one for her head and a smaller one for her body.

2

Draw two big white circles on her face and make her body light brown.

3

Add light brown pointed ears and dark brown wings. Give her a dark brown chest as well.

4

Finish her off with two beady black eyes, an orange beak, and little orange feet.

If you like, give her a warm knitted hat...

...and a few feathers.

Light it up!

Draw a line joining up all of the lights with even numbers. Start at the arrow at the bottom of the tree and finish at the star on the top.

18

12

6

14   33

42

16   38

8

22

11   36

35

17   16   7

28   9   19

10

5   24

6   47   28   36

46   16   14

25

31

19   29   8   10

22   46   25

36   23   11

15

13   19   18   10   16   12 ← START

7

70

SMILE PLEASE!

Which of these smiley faces appears more than twice?

71

SNOW WAY!

Look carefully at the order of the three snowflakes below. How many times can you find them in exactly the same order in the box? Search from left to right, and from top to bottom.

up to mischief

Can you find a hat, shoe, collar, and belt in the picture below?
Which elf do they belong to?

a   b   c   d   e

DOMINO EFFECT

The penguins love playing games! Which of the three red dominoes on the right completes the line at the bottom?

What's in a name?

Santa has so many elves that he sometimes can't remember all their names. Using the clues, can you draw lines to match each elf sister above to her brother below and work out all their names?

My brother has blond hair.

Plum and Kiki have red hats.

My brother has a red hat.

My brother has a red hat.

My sister has no candy cane.

My sister has a candy cane.

Ruby and Kiki have candy canes.

My sister's name is Lulu.

Noel

Milo

Rudi

Chip

Little Donkey...

These little donkeys may look the same at first glance, but each one differs in one small way from the others. Can you spot all the differences?

STOCKING UP!

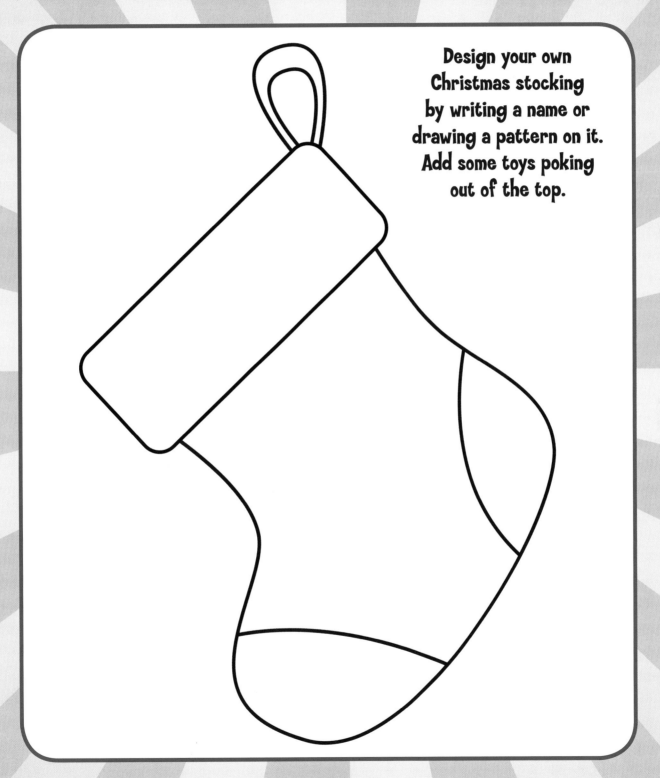

Design your own Christmas stocking by writing a name or drawing a pattern on it. Add some toys poking out of the top.

a defug

b insiar

c yerrch

d foefet

e hocc pich

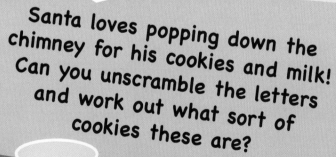

f tupnea

Santa loves popping down the chimney for his cookies and milk! Can you unscramble the letters and work out what sort of cookies these are?

Christmas wish

Join the dots to see what kind of toy Santa has brought for Lilly.

It's just what I always wanted!

Hit the right note!

Someone in the choir is singing out of tune! Can you tell which note is the odd one out and why?

DING DONG MERRILY...

How many bells can you see?

WINTER WARMER

Look carefully at this festive scene, then answer the questions on the opposite page.

WINTER WARMER QUESTIONS

1. How many Christmas stockings can you see?

2. How many Santa hats are in the picture?

3. How many candy canes can you count?

4. How many candles can you count?

5. How many parcels appear in the picture?

6. How many bells can you see?

7. How many gold stars appear in the picture?

8. How many blue baubles can you count?

Count carefully!

Polar poser...

Draw a circle around the odd snowflake out.

ANSWERS

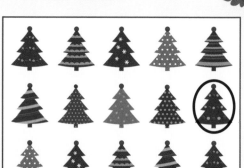

Page 4   NUTTY NUTCRACKERS

Answer = **D**
He has a gold buckle not a white one.

Page 5   STAINED GLASS ANGEL

Page 6   MERRY MAZE

Page 7   FIR TREE FOREST

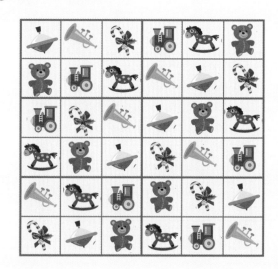

Page 8   A BIRD IN THE HAND

Answer = **E**
In shadow A, the parcel bow is missing; in shadow B, one of the light bulbs has disappeared; in shadow C, the bird has lost the bobble from his hat; shadow D's bird has lost part of his tail.

Page 9   TOY-DOKU

Page 11   COOKIE TIME!

Answer = **C**

Page 12   FESTIVE FROLICS

Page 15   LET IT SNOW!

Page 16   SLEIGH RIDE

In picture B:
1. One of Rudolph's antlers is missing.
2. The moon is facing in the opposite direction.
3. Santa's mittens are black.
4. Santa's sack is purple.
5. A tree behind Rudolph is missing.
6. Rudolph's saddle is blue not green.

Page 17   DOTTY DILEMMA

Page 19   MUFFIN MAYHEM

Answers:
A = chocolate; B = raspberry; C = blueberry;
D = vanilla; E = strawberry; F = banana

Page 20   THE REAL RUDOLPH

Answer = **B**

Page 21   STUFFED STOCKINGS

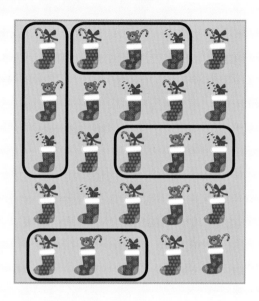

Page 22   JINGLE BELLS

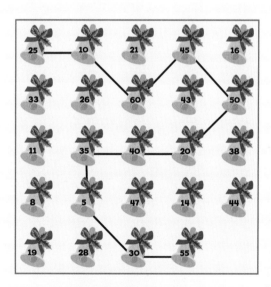

Page 24   SNOW TIME!

Page 25   SECRET SILHOUETTE

Page 26   BOOT-IFUL BOOTS

Page 27 MAZE DAZE

Page 28 IT'S A GIFT...

Answers:
A = train; B = teddy; C = ball; D = dolly; E = bricks;
F = toy car

Page 29 SOCK IT TO ME!

Page 31 WOODLAND WONDER

In picture B:
1. The owl's hat has changed from red to yellow.
2. The squirrel's nut has turned into a strawberry.
3. The robin is missing from the top of the Christmas tree.
4. One of the Christmas tree lights has disappeared.
5. The fox has lost his tail.
6. The deer's antlers have changed to black.

Page 32 SLEIGH BELLS IN THE SNOW

Answer = **D**
In shadow A, Rudolph has lost his antlers; Santa is missing the bobble from his hat in shadow B; in shadow C, the sledge runner is much shorter; in shadow E, Rudolph has lost his tail.

Page 33 CANDY QUEST

Answer = **12**

Page 34 CHRISTMAS FAIRIES

Answer = **C**

ANSWERS

Page 35 FESTIVE FOLK

Page 36 ALL WRAPPED UP

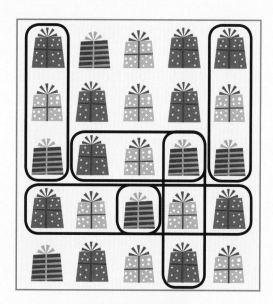

Page 38 SHAD-OKU TIME!

Page 39 COOL SHADES

Page 40 KNOTTY PROBLEM

Answer = **C**

ANSWERS

Page 41 POLES APART!

Page 42 SWEET TOOTH

Answers:
A = orange; B = cola; C = mint; D = plum;
E = lime; F = lemon (or melon!)

Page 44 COUNTING STARS

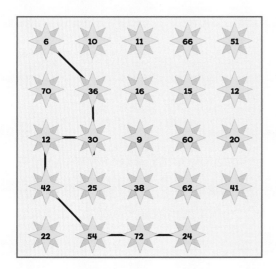

Page 45 SHADOW PUPPETS

Answer: **B**
In shadow A, the left hand star is missing; in shadow C, the puppet's hands have disappeared;

in shadow D, the oval shape of one of the decorations has disappeared; in shadow E, the string of the puppet is missing.

Page 46 TOY STORY

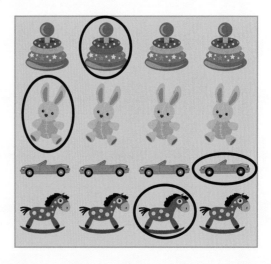

Page 47 WE THREE KINGS...

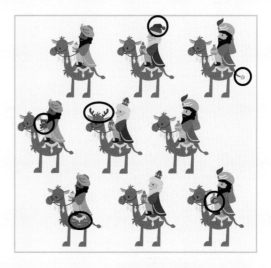

Answers: **A, F,** and **H** are the real Wise Men. Wise Man B is wearing a knitted hat; Wise Man C's camel has a bell on the end of his tail; Wise Man D is holding a teddy bear; Wise Man E's camel has antlers; Wise Man G's saddle has baubles instead of tassels; Wise Man I is wearing mittens.

Page 48   COOKIES GALORE!

Answers:
Gingerbread man
Bell
Star
Heart

Pages 51-52   SNOW GLOBE POSER

Answers:
1. Seven.
2. Two.
3. A Christmas tree.
4. A Christmas wreath.
5. A broom.

Page 53   LOOK THROUGH THE WINDOW

Page 54   A-MAZE-ING!

Page 55   NUTCRACKER ARMY

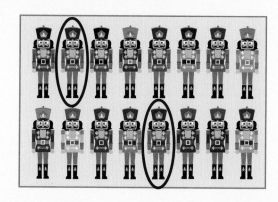

Page 56   MONKEY PUZZLE

Answer = **C**
His buttons are green.

Page 58   CANDY-DOKU

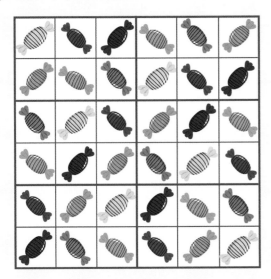

Page 59   WHILE SHEPHERDS WATCHED...

Page 60   MISSING PIECE...

Answer = **D**

Page 61   WINTER WONDERLAND

In picture B:
1. The dog has gone missing.
2. The snowman has lost his broom.
3. The chimney on the house far right has disappeared.
4. The sledger's hat has changed from red to green.
5. The arched window is missing from the house on the left.
6. There is no star at the top of the Christmas tree.

Page 62   GET YOUR SKATES ON!

Page 63   NUMBER FUN

Answers:

A = **32**
As you move from left to right, double the previous number to get the next one along.

B = **17**
As you move from left to right, add 3 to each number to get the next one along.

C = **23**
As you move from left to right, add 1 to the first number, then 2 to the second, then 3 to the third, etc.

Page 65   MAKING TRACKS

Page 66   PUPPET ON A STRING

Answer = **B**

Page 68   SWEET TREATS

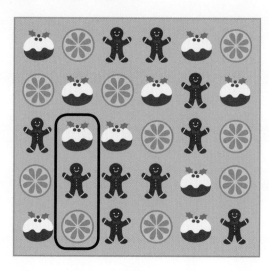

Page 70   LIGHT IT UP!

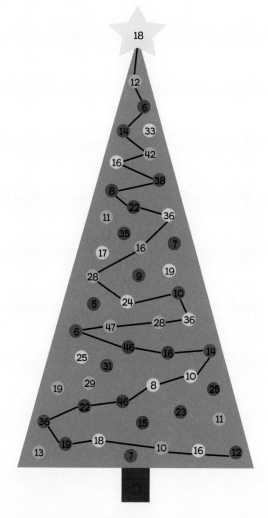

Page 71   SMILE PLEASE!

Page 72   SNOW WAY!

Page 73   UP TO MISCHIEF

Answer = **D**
He has green boots, a red collar, a brown belt, and a hat with points and a bell.

Page 74   DOMINO EFFECT

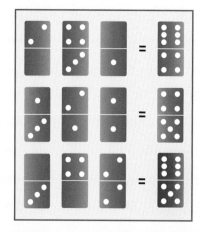

Answer = **A**
The dots on the dominoes in the last column equal the total of all the other dots in the same row.

Page 75   WHAT'S IN A NAME?

Answers:
A = Lulu. Her brother is Chip.
B = Ruby. Her brother is Rudi.
C = Plum. Her brother is Noel.
D = Kiki. Her brother is Milo.

ANSWERS

Page 76   LITTLE DONKEY...

Page 78   CRUNCH TIME

Answers:
A = fudge; B = raisin; C = cherry; D = toffee
E = choc chip; F = peanut

Page 79   CHRISTMAS WISH

Page 80   HIT THE RIGHT NOTE!

Answer = **37**
All the other numbers are from the seven times table.

Page 81   DING DONG MERRILY...

Answer = **12**

Pages 82–83   WINTER WARMER

Answers:
1. Three: one on the wreath; one on the tree; one on the fireplace.
2. Two: one on the floor; one on the fireplace.
3. Seven: three on the wreath; two on the tree; two on the fireplace.
4. Two: both on the fireplace.
5. Eight: five on the floor; three on the fireplace.
6. Three: one on the tree; two on the fireplace.
7. Eight: five on the wreath; two on the tree; one on the fireplace.
8. Three: one in the parcel; one on the fireplace; one hanging from the ceiling.

Page 84   POLAR POSER